Storytime Discoveries

Read-Aloud Stories and Demonstrations About
Physical Science

Written by Dotti Enderle

Illustrated by Ginger Illustration

Teaching & Learning Company

1204 Buchanan St., P.O. Box 10
Carthage, IL 62321-0010

This book belongs to

_____

Cover design by Jennifer Morgan

Copyright © 2003, Teaching & Learning Company

ISBN No. 1-57310-388-8

Printing No. 987654321

Teaching & Learning Company
1204 Buchanan St., P.O. Box 10
Carthage, IL 62321-0010

Table of Contents

iii

Dear Teacher or Parent,

It's never too early to introduce children to science. Little eyes are curious, and what child hasn't taken apart a toy from time to time simply to see how it works? Science experiments hold a world of wonder.

Conducting science experiments in the classroom makes you not only the teacher, but master magician as well; holding small minds as mesmerized and awed as if you were Houdini himself.

Combining science experiments with Storytime is a teaching method long overdue. Storytime is a time of absorption for children. Many lessons are learned in stories, whether moral or academic. Choosing to conduct science experiments during this critical time in childhood development gives children a reference point, helping them to visually relate to the story as well as introducing them to scientific laws and principles surrounding their world.

Storytime Discoveries: Physical Science contains a collection of original stories, folktales and poems, each dealing with the science of physics. The experiments are simple to conduct and require ordinary ingredients, usually found in the kitchen. Several of the experiments contain optional presentation ideas, should you wish to be more theatrical. Feel free to come up with your own embellishments, especially if you are performing for a larger group.

Though small children may not fully comprehend molecules, matter or energy, they are fully aware of the forces surrounding them and delight in the smallest scientific fact. Whether it's a squeaky balloon or a misshapen shadow, there is no better time for discovery than early childhood. Prepare ahead of time, be ready for cleanup and most of all have fun!

Sincerely,

Dotti Enderle

The Famous Feud of Mason Jar Gulch

Materials

clear jar with a
screw-top lid filled
half-full with water
cooking oil
liquid detergent
spoon

Presentation Idea

Turn your liquid detergent bottle into the sheriff with a badge cut from aluminum foil and handlebar moustache made out of yarn or construction paper.

Explanation

The molecules of oil stick together, and when added to water form a separate layer that floats. The soap surrounds the oil droplets, and traps them so they can't join together. This forces them to be distributed and suspended in the water.

Directions

1. Pour oil into the water at designated intervals, cap and shake.

2. Squirt in liquid detergent.

3. Stir with spoon.

The Famous Feud of Mason Jar Gulch

Mason Jar Gulch is now a peaceful town. But the people still talk about a famous feud that took place there many years ago.

On the south side of town lived a family named Waterbottom. They were the largest, most respected family in Mason Jar Gulch. *(Pour some oil in the jar of water and wait a moment for it to rise to the top.)*

On the north side of town lived a family named Oiltop. The Oiltops were a slippery bunch, but they kept to themselves.

Then one day the Oiltops decided to visit the other side of town. *(Stir oil and water with the spoon.)* They rode down south and met up with the Waterbottoms. Well, the chemistry just wasn't right between these two, and the minute they saw each other things got messy.

"Oiltops! We don't want you here," Papa Waterbottom yelled. "Get back where you belong!"

The Oiltops quickly rode back up to the north part of town.

Pa Oiltop paced back and forth. "They can't bully us like that," he said. "Let's slide on back down there and show them who's boss." *(Stir oil and water with the spoon.)*

Again, the Oiltops rode down to the south side of Mason Jar Gulch.

"Oh, you're slick," said Papa Waterbottom. "Think you can come down here and take over, huh? Well forget it!"

The Waterbottoms again ran the Oiltops away from their part of town.

The Oiltops were furious. "The Waterbottoms may be a respected family in this community, but we have rights, too," Pa Oiltop said. "Come on, let's fry 'em!"

But the Waterbottoms were also having a meeting. "You know the Oiltops won't stop without a fight," Papa Waterbottom said. "When they come back, we'll be ready. We'll boil 'em!" *(Screw the lid on the jar.)*

When the Oiltops rode back down, it caused a great ruckus. *(Shake the jar to mix oil and water.)* The whole town was shaken up. But the Waterbottoms and the Oiltops could not dissolve their differences. *(Set the jar down so the oil and water will separate again.)*

Fear spread through Mason Jar Gulch. Folks were jittery and on edge. They knew the Oiltops were planning the right moment to strike, and the Waterbottoms were waiting for them. Something had to be done.

That's when Sheriff Suds rode in. *(Hold up detergent bottle.)* "I aim to clean up this town," he said. *(Take the lid off the jar.)*

Sheriff Suds waited. The Waterbottoms were steaming on their side of town. The Oiltops were sizzling on theirs. When things got too hot to handle, they struck again. *(Stir quickly with the spoon.)*

"Oh no, you don't," said Sheriff Suds. "Take this!" *(Squirt a stream of detergent into the oil and water, screw on the lid and shake vigorously.)*

The whole town went topsy-turvy. It was not a pleasant sight. *(Set the jar down and take off the lid.)* But in the end the Oiltops broke down. "We shouldn't have tried to take over the south side of town," they cried.

"No, it's our fault," sobbed the Waterbottoms. "We shouldn't have tried to drown you out!"

After that, the Waterbottoms and the Oiltops mixed and mingled. And they lived happily together in the shining town of Mason Jar Gulch.

The Crow and the Pitcher

Materials

small, clear plastic pitcher filled three-fourths full with water
marbles

Presentation Idea

Turn your hand into a crow puppet.

You will need a black mitten or glove, glue and two small white buttons or pom-poms.

Place the mitten on your hand. Position the buttons for eyes and glue in place. Make the crow talk and pick up marbles by moving your thumb (lower beak) against your fingers (upper beak).

Directions

At designated intervals, drop the marbles into the pitcher of water.

Explanation

The marbles add volume to the pitcher, displacing the water and causing it to rise.

The Crow and the Pitcher

An Aesop Fable

A thirsty crow flew about searching for water. "Caw! Caw!" he coughed through his dry throat. No fountains! No puddles! No water anywhere! But then, just as he soared over a picnic table, he spotted a pitcher half full of water. He flew down and perched on the side of the pitcher, but when he tried to take a drink, he couldn't reach the water! *(Place your hand on the rim of the pitcher and try to dip your fingers in to demonstrate.)*

Oh no! the crow thought. There's got to be a way I can get to that water.

He tried pecking the side of the pitcher to break it *(Tap the side of the pitcher.)*, but that didn't work. He tried pushing against the pitcher to overturn it *(Pretend to push against the pitcher.)*, but he didn't have the strength. All that work just made him thirstier. The crow gave up and flew on.

Not far from the picnic area he saw a lovely rock garden. That gave him a wonderful idea. The crow swooped down and picked up a pebble. He carried it to the pitcher and dropped it in. *(Pick up a marble and drop it in the pitcher.)* He went back and got another pebble and dropped it into the pitcher, too. *(Drop another marble in the pitcher.)* Then he got another, and another and another.

(Continue to drop in the marbles until the water rises to the top.) One by one, he dropped the pebbles into the pitcher. Slowly, the water rose higher and higher. The thirsty crow leaned down and took a long, cool drink. *(Place your hand on the side of the pitcher and dip your fingers in.)*

"Ahhhh," he said, "that's better."

The crow then flew off in search of food. *(Cross your wrists and flitter your fingers in the motion of a bird flying.)*

The Queen's Jubilee

Materials

three glasses of the same size, two half-filled with water
red food coloring
blue food coloring

Explanation

Mixing primary colors (red, blue and yellow) produces secondary colors (purple, orange and green).

Directions

1. Squeeze several drops of red food coloring into one glass of water.
2. Squeeze several drops of blue food coloring into the other glass of water.
3. Pour the contents of both glasses together in the empty glass.

10

The Queen's Jubilee

The Queen's jubilee was only a month away, and she wanted everything to be perfect. After all, she had been Queen for 25 years! The party would take place in the palace, with only the finest for her kingdom. Chefs were working around the clock, planning the perfect feast. Decorators were designing streamers and banners to hang from the ceiling. Even the musicians had been hired, and were rehearsing 12 hours a day. The jubilee would be awesome.

Of course the Queen wanted a magnificent robe to match this great occasion. She sought out the two best tailors in the land, Joseph and Samuel.

"My robe must be a most regal color," she insisted. "I want to shine as brightly as my crown!"

The tailors hurried back to their sewing rooms and began sorting the cloth.

"Ah!" said Joseph. "The queen must wear red. *(Squeeze several drops of red food coloring into one of the glasses of water.)* Red is perfect!"

"Red?" Samuel said, stroking his pointy beard.

"Yes," Joseph continued. "Red will highlight the rosy glow of her cheeks. And it is the color of an autumn sunset. What is more regal than the color red?"

"Blue!" Samuel blurted. *(Squeeze several drops of the blue food coloring into the other glass of water.)* "Blue is the color of the sky and the sea. There is nothing more majestic than the sky and the sea. And blue will bring out the color of her royal blue eyes."

"I think it should be red!" Joseph demanded. "Red is more befitting a queen."

"No, blue!" Samuel argued.

"Red!"

"Blue!"

"Red!"

"Blue!"

This went on day after day, until the eve of the Queen's jubilee. She entered the sewing room and called, "I'm ready for my robe! Joseph? Samuel? Where are you?"

The two tailors hid behind a table of cloth, shaking with fear.

"Oh no," Samuel whispered. "We'll lose our heads for sure."

"Maybe not," Joseph said. He stood up and faced the queen. "Your highness, Samuel and I haven't made the robe yet. We were afraid to make it so soon. We didn't want to risk it getting soiled."

"What?" the queen shouted, her royal blue eyes turning a stormy gray.

"But," Samuel said, poking his head up from behind the table. "We'll work all night, you'll have it first thing in the morning."

The Queen stood tall, glaring down at them. "You better have it ready before the cock crows."

The tailors bowed. "Certainly, your Highness."

Samuel stepped forward, holding the blue material. *(Hold up the glass of blue water.)* I suggest we use this lovely blue. It's the most regal color there is."

"No, no!" Joseph said, stumbling forward. *(Hold up the glass of red water.)* Red is the most regal, don't you think?"

The queen looked from one color to the next. Back and forth, her eyes darted, until she appeared dizzy. "Oh brother!" she said. "Just put them together!"

(Pour the red and blue water together into the empty glass to make purple.)

And that's exactly what the tailors did. To their amazement, they created the most regal color of all.

A Very Anxious Octopus

A very anxious octopus
As uptight as can be
Could not relax on sand or rock,
But only in the sea.

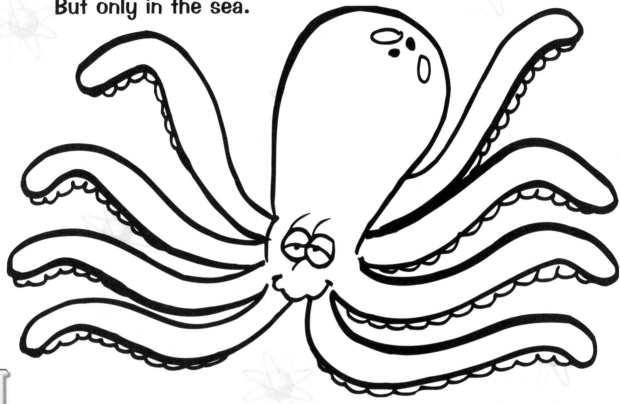

Materials

scissors
crayons or markers
pencil
bowl of water

Explanation

The paper is lightweight and conforms to the round pencil. When wet, the paper fibers fill with water, weighing it down and straightening the curls.

Directions

1. Color and cut out the octopus.
2. Use the pencil to curl all his tentacles.
3. Place him in the bowl of water, and the tentacles will relax and straighten out.

The King Who Wished to Bite the Moon

Materials

set of wooden or plastic blocks

Explanation

The blocks tumble because structures have little resistance when being pulled apart at the supporting base.

Directions

1. Stack blocks at designated times in the story.
2. Carefully remove the bottom block.

The King Who Wished to Bite the Moon

Based on a Caribbean Folktale

In a kingdom far away, but not too far, lived a King who loved to watch the sky. Many nights he sat on his balcony, looking at the moon and the stars, wondering what they were. His curiosity grew and grew until he couldn't stand another moment of not knowing. He called in the Grand Wizard, Elmore.

"Elmore," he said, pacing the floor. "I must know and I must know now! What exactly are the stars?"

Elmore, who was more of a grand imposter than a grand wizard, looked up at the Big Dipper. "Ah!" he sighed, conjuring a fib. "The stars are fireflies who've lost their way. See how they twinkle like their cousins in the field?"

This satisfied the King, who smiled. "Yes. Of course. But what about the moon? What is the moon?"

Elmore stroked his chin as he studied the moon. "Your Majesty, look. Isn't it obvious? The moon is just a large cookie."

"A cookie?" the King exclaimed. "How in the world did it get up in the sky?"

Elmore pondered this question a moment then said, "It probably floated up from a magical oven."

The King never stopped to think about whether or not this could be possible. "Fine, then," said the King. "A cookie that big is surely meant for a King. I must take a bite!"

Elmore gulped. He knew the King was not finished with him.

"Elmore, you shall help me reach the moon so I can have a taste."

"B-b-but, your Majesty," Elmore stuttered. "How will you reach it?"

The King shook his head, giving Elmore a steely look. "A brilliant wizard like yourself should have to ask such a silly question? It's simple. We'll stack all the boxes in the kingdom, one on top of the other. Then I'll climb up for my snack. Now, waste no more of my time. Quickly, gather some horsemen and ride door to door, asking everyone to lend the King their boxes and trunks."

Elmore did as he was told, and soon the courtyard was littered with boxes. He watched the next day as the King's work-men busied themselves stacking the boxes. One . . . two . . . three . . . *(Begin stacking blocks.)* four . . . five . . . six . . . *(Stack about half of the blocks.)*

That night, as the moon rose higher into the sky, the King made his entrance into the courtyard. His entire kingdom was there to watch. The King climbed up the boxes, carefully watching his footing so he wouldn't fall. When he reached the top, he stood on his tiptoes, and tried to grab the moon. The boxes weren't nearly high enough.

"I need more boxes!" the King shouted to Elmore.

"But there are no more boxes," Elmore shouted back. "We've used every box in the kingdom."

The King hurried down to the bottom. "Then chop down the trees and make new ones!"

The next day, every worker in the kingdom busied himself, cutting trees and making boxes. It was a noisy affair, but the King didn't mind. He could only think about that giant cookie in the sky.

That night, many more boxes were scattered in the courtyard. The King watched as the workmen stacked the rest of the boxes. *(Stack the remaining blocks on top of the others.)* Seven . . . eight . . . nine . . . . The tower of boxes was enormous!

The King again climbed carefully to the very top. He stood on his tiptoes and reached for the moon. "I can almost reach it!" he shouted down through the clouds. "Just barely! I need one more box!"

"But, your Majesty!" Elmore shouted up at the King. "There is not a single box left in the kingdom!"

"Then make one more!"

"Your Majesty! We've cut down all the trees! There is no wood left to make a box!"

The King felt his anger rising inside him. He had to get a bite of this cookie! "Elmore! Are you not a grand wizard?"

Elmore wondered if this was a test. "Uh . . . why yes."

"The answer is simple," the King said. "Take the bottom box and send it up!"

"But, your majesty!" Elmore shouted.

"Don't argue, Elmore. Send up that bottom box or I'll have your head!"

Elmore drooped. He looked at the workers and nodded. They bent down and removed the bottom box. *(Take away the bottom block so the stack topples.)* And, of course, the King never got his bite of the moon.

Honest Abe

Materials

tarnished penny
$1/2$ cup of vinegar
1 teaspoon of salt

Presentation Idea

You can present this story as a fingerplay.

You will need two gardening gloves; black construction paper; small amounts of yarn cut into 2" lengths in black, yellow, brown and red; felt-tipped markers and glue.

The index finger of one glove will be Abe. Give him a black construction paper stovepipe hat. Draw on a face and beard with the markers. All five digits on the other glove will be the children. Glue on yarn hair and draw on faces with the markers.

Explanation

Vinegar is four to eight percent acetic acid, which dissolves mineral deposits and corrosion. Salt is an abrasive. Working together, they eat away at the tarnish, which is not dirt, but a transformed state of the penny's copper.

Directions

1. Mix salt in the cup of vinegar.
2. At the designated time, drop the penny in the salt/vinegar solution.
3. At the end of the story, take the penny out to show how shiny it is.

Honest Abe

Do you know the man on this penny? He is Abraham Lincoln, the 16th President of the United States.

Abraham Lincoln was born in a log cabin on February 12, 1809. His family were hardworking farmers.

Children: That's good!

No, that was bad because farmwork kept them so busy, Abraham could not go to school.

Children: That's bad!

No, that was good because Abraham taught himself to read.

Children: That's good!

No, that was bad because he had to walk for miles just to borrow books!

Children: That's bad!

No, that was good because it taught him how valuable books were. It also taught him to be friendly, to be a good storyteller and to be honest. People called him "Honest Abe."

Children: That's good!

No, that was bad because he was so honest, he wanted to change everything that was wrong. And something was terribly wrong in our country then. Times were tarnished and dark *(Hold up the penny as an example of tarnish.)* because of a thing called "slavery." People owned other people the way they'd own an animal. Abe was so honest, he just knew this was wrong.

Children: That's bad!

Yes, that was bad, but Abe decided to change things. (Drop the penny in the salt/vinegar solution.) He read many, many law books and became a lawyer. The people trusted him so much, they elected him as a U.S. senator. And later he became President!

Children: That's good!

No, that was bad because after Abraham Lincoln became President, the country had a war. It was called the Civil War. The southern states fought against the northern states. The war lasted four years!

Children: That's bad!

No, that was good because Abraham Lincoln would not give up. He ended slavery in the United States.

Children: That's good!

Yes, that was very good! *(Take the penny from the solution and show the children how shiny it is.)* And that is why Abraham Lincoln "shined" as our 16th President. He ended the war and gave freedom to many people.

What Did Jeremy See?

Directions

When instructed in the story, place each object on the overhead to cast a shadow.

Explanation

A shadow is produced when a solid object passes between a light source and the direction the light is cast.

What Did Jeremy See?

Jeremy's father gave him a big hug and tucked him in bed. "I want you to go right to sleep." he said.

"Okay," Jeremy said with a smile.

His father turned out the light and left the room. *(Turn out the light in the room and turn on the overhead.)* Outside a street lamp glowed, and a stream of light shone in Jeremy's window. Strange shadows danced on the wall. His smile soon faded.

(Place the comb on the overhead.) Jeremy saw huge monster teeth ready to take a bite.

What did Jeremy see?

Children: A comb!

(Place the scissors on the overhead, slightly open.) Then Jeremy saw a large alligator crawling across the floor.

What did Jeremy see?

Children: Scissors!

(Place the spoon on the overhead.) Jeremy gasped when a ghost flew through the air.

What did Jeremy see?

Children: A spoon!

(Place the pretzel on the overhead.) Jeremy couldn't believe his eyes. A fat bullfrog had hopped into his room.

What did Jeremy see?

Children: A pretzel!

(Place the hairbrush on the overhead.) The Wolfman sat waiting in the corner.

What did Jeremy see?

Children: A brush!

(Place the jar lid on the overhead.) A flying saucer landed near Jeremy's bed. Alien spacemen were sure to take him away to another planet.

What did Jeremy see?

Children: A lid!

(Place the piece of string on the overhead.) A snake slithered in, ready to strike!

What did Jeremy see?

Children: Some string!

(Place the tweezers on the overhead.) Jeremy jerked the covers up to his chin when he saw sharp, vampire fangs.

What did Jeremy see?

Children: Tweezers!

(Place the marble on the overhead.) An evil eye stared at Jeremy!

What did Jeremy see?

Children: A marble!

(Place the glove on the overhead.) A giant's hand reached out for him!

What did Jeremy see?

Children: A glove!

(Place the gingerbread man cookie cutter on the overhead.) Jeremy's father walked into the room. He flipped the switch. *(Turn on the light in the room.)*

Children: Do you know what Jeremy saw?

The light!

Humpty Dumpty's Great Fall

Materials

hard-boiled egg, shelled
1 quart juice bottle
matches

Presentation Idea

Draw Humpty Dumpty's face
on the egg with a permanent
marker.

Explanation

The flame uses up oxygen, which
reduces air pressure inside the bottle.
This makes the air pressure greater
outside the bottle, and it pushes the
egg in.

Directions

1. Shell the egg before
   starting.
2. Hold up the egg to
   represent Humpty
   Dumpty.
3. Strike a match and
   drop it into the bottle.
4. Place the egg on the
   mouth of the bottle.

Humpty Dumpty's Great Fall

Remember when Humpty Dumpty sat on a wall? Remember when Humpty Dumpty had a great fall? Humpty's shell cracked into a million pieces, but he wasn't hurt. Humpty was hard-boiled. *(Show egg.)*

"I'm tired," Humpty said, looking around for a place to sit. "That wall is too risky. I need a safer place."

So, Humpty Dumpty went searching for a good spot to sit down. He spotted a bench near the park. *This looks perfect,* he thought. But once he sat down, the strips of wood pinched his bottom.

"Ouch!" he cried, hopping up quickly.

Then Humpty saw a picnic table.

"I could sit on that," he said.

Humpty jumped up on the table, but the table leaned, and he rolled right off.

"Why is it so hard for me to sit down?" Humpty wondered as he wobbled away.

Soon he came to a fence.

"Maybe I could sit there."

But on closer inspection, he saw that the rails were too spiky. He didn't even try. Humpty plopped on the ground and looked around. He saw swings and slides, birdbaths and mailboxes, trees and bushes. Nothing looked comfortable enough to sit on. Then, Humpty looked up. High on a rooftop stood a tall, brick chimney.

"I could sit there!" Humpty shouted.

He carefully climbed to the top of the house, unaware that there was a roaring fire in the fireplace. *(Strike a match and drop it in the bottle.)* As soon as Humpty sat down, *(Place the egg on the mouth of the bottle and the lack of oxygen will pull it inside.)* Pop! In he went!

"Oh no!" Humpty groaned. "Not again!"

Goldilocks Upside Down

Materials

shiny, stainless steel spoon for each child

Explanation

When light bounces from your face to a mirror or shiny object, then back to your eyes, that's reflection. The concave shape of the spoon's bowl bounces the light at different angles, causing the reflection to appear upside down.

Directions

At designated times in the story, have the children look at their reflection in the bowl of the spoon, then on the back of the spoon.

Goldilocks Upside Down

At lunchtime, Mama Bear made some delicious chicken noodle soup. "Come eat," she called to Papa Bear and Baby Bear. But when they sat down and took a bite, Baby Bear said, "Ouch! This soup is too hot!"

"Let's go for a walk and let it cool off," Papa Bear suggested.

So the three bears took a walk in the woods.

They weren't gone long when a curious little girl named Goldilocks knocked at their door.

"Is anybody home?" she called. "Hello?"

Goldilocks opened the door and peeked in. She tiptoed to the kitchen and saw three bowls of soup sitting on the table.

"Ummmm, that smells good," she said, sitting down in front of the biggest bowl.

She was about to take a sip when she glimpsed her reflection in the spoon. *(Have each child look into the bowl of the spoon.)* Goldilocks was upside down!

"Oh no!" she cried, "I'm standing on my head!"

She dropped the spoon and looked around.

"Hmmmm . . . everything looks right side up."

She picked up the spoon again and looked at her reflection. She was still upside down.

"Not again!" she said. "It's a good thing I didn't try to eat the soup. I might have spilled it."

She got up and walked around the room.

"I'm still on the floor," she said. "And the ceiling is still above me."

She sat back down and grabbed the spoon. When she looked inside it, she was upside down again. Goldilocks started to cry.

Just then, the three bears came home. They saw a strange little girl sobbing at their table.

"What's wrong?" Mama Bear asked.

Goldilocks sobbed. "I want to eat some of this delicious soup," she said, "but every time I try, I turn upside down. See?"

Goldilocks held the spoon up to her face where Mama Bear could see.

"Oh," said Mama Bear, with a smile. "I can fix that."

Mama Bear took the spoon and turned it around to the other side. *(Turn the spoon so the children can see their reflections on the back.)* "Look again."

Goldilocks saw herself right side up.

"Now, would you like to join us for lunch?" Mama Bear asked.

"Yes, thank you," Goldilocks said.

Mama Bear put another bowl of soup on the table, and they gobbled it right up!

Skating Skunk

Slink, slunk, Stinky Skunk
Is nothing like the others.
He slips and slides,
And skates and glides,
And floats before his brothers!

Materials

scissors
crayons or markers
aluminum pop-top ring
    tabs
rubber cement
baking pan
water

Explanation

The surface tension of the water is like a thick skin that supports the ring tabs when they lay sideways.

Directions

1. Color and cut out the skunk.
2. Fold in half and bend the feet flat.
3. Glue the aluminum ring tabs to the bottom of the skunk's feet.
4. When the glue is dry, fill the baking pan nearly full with water.
5. Carefully set the skunk on the water surface, and he'll float.

How Cats Got Their Purr

Materials

large two-hole button
18" to 24" of thin string or
strong thread

Explanation

The law of inertia—a body in
motion tends to stay in motion.
The vibration of the string causes
the sound.

Directions

1. Thread the string through the button-holes and tie a knot at the end.
2. Center the button.
3. Loop string on each side of your index finger.
4. Wind the button in a clockwise or counter-clockwise motion.
5. Pull string taut so the button will spin, making a purring noise.

How Cats Got Their Purr
An English Folktale

The King and Queen were the proudest people in the kingdom. They had a new baby girl! The baby, named Lila, had the finest things that any child could want. And her royal parents made sure she was happy all the time. But the Queen worried about her daughter constantly, so to set her mind at ease, she sought out a gypsy fortune teller.

The old fortune teller gave the Queen some dreadful news. "Oh, dear! This is terrible!" she said, gazing into her crystal ball. "When Princess Lila is grown she will marry a Prince."

"Of course," the Queen said, wondering how that could be so bad.

"Nothing could be worse," the gypsy continued. "Princess Lila will live in sorrow and pain, spending most of her life with a broken heart."

The Queen couldn't bear to think of her daughter in any kind of pain. "What can I do to prevent this tragedy?"

The old woman consulted her crystal ball again. "You must find three pure white cats for Lila to play with. Keep the cats with her always. When the time comes, things will work themselves out."

The Queen thanked the old woman, then quickly sent her servants throughout the kingdom in search of three pure white cats. When the cats arrived, Lila was delighted! They stayed by her always, even sleeping in her crib.

Many years later, as predicted, Lila grew up and fell in love with a Prince. Prince Timothy loved her, too, and they were happily married. But Timothy had made an enemy of a neighboring king—King Silbert. The wicked King Silbert kidnapped Prince Timothy and locked him deep in the castle dungeon.

Lila spent her days crying in sorrow and filled with pain. The only comfort she had were the three white cats. But Lila was much stronger than the old gypsy could ever have known. She gathered her cats into a large basket and headed for the neighboring kingdom to rescue her husband.

Once inside King Silbert's castle, she decided to strike a bargain. "Please tell me, what I must do in exchange for the release of Prince Timothy."

King Silbert sneered. He looked about his bare, cold castle. The walls were decorated with steel swords, axes and armor. But unlike other castles, there were no lovely tapestries to give it color. He twirled his mustache and said, "I'll provide a spinning wheel for you in the tower. You'll have until Midwinter's Day to spin 10,000 skeins of wool. If you spin just one skein less, you'll never see Prince Timothy again."

"But that's impossible!" Lila cried. "Midwinter's Day is just three weeks away!"

King Silbert shook his head. "Then take your cats and go home."

"No, wait! I must try."

King Silbert curled his lips and grinned through crooked brown teeth. "Remember, 10,000 skeins. And no other hands can touch it—just yours."

Lila was taken to the tower, where a large spinning wheel stood before her. She quickly threaded it *(Thread the string through the buttonholes, and tie a knot at the end. Center the button. Loop the string on each side of your index fingers.)* and began to spin. *(Swing the button to wind it, in a slow motion like turning a jump rope. Swing it either clockwise or counterclockwise, but always in the same direction.)*

She spun for three days, barely stopping. But she grew tired and weary, and realized that she could never spin 10,000 skeins by Midwinter's Day. She fell to the floor and cried herself to sleep. She awoke later to the whirling sound of the spinning wheel. *(Separate your hands pulling the string taut. Then bring your hands together, releasing it. Pull and release, causing the button to spin quickly, winding and rewinding on its own.)* Her mouth popped open in amazement when she saw one of her cats spinning the wool!

At first Lila panicked. She remembered King Silbert's warning that no other hands should touch the spinning wheel. But she quickly relaxed. Cats don't have hands; they have paws.

(Continue to keep the button spinning.)

The cats took turns, spinning and spinning. And by Midwinter's Day, all 10,000 skeins of wool were woven.

King Silbert was outraged, but a bargain is a bargain. He let Prince Timothy go.

Soon after, King Silbert's kingdom was overthrown. He was run out of his country and never allowed to return.

Princess Lila and Prince Timothy lived happily ever after with their three cats. And as a reward, the cats were given the gift of purring to show their contentment. How strange that their purr sounds very much like the whirling of a spinning wheel!

(Hold the spinning button near each child's ear so he can hear the purring noise made by the spinning button and string.)

Whining Wendy

Materials

balloon

Presentation Idea

Draw Wendy's face on the balloon with a felt-tipped marker.

Explanation

The vibration of air traveling through the neck of the balloon produces sound. The smaller the passage, the higher pitched the sound becomes.

Directions

1. Blow up the balloon, but don't tie it off.
2. Hold the balloon between your thumbs and index fingers.
3. Slowly pull the neck of the balloon to release enough air to make noise.

34

Whining Wendy

Wendy drove her parents crazy! Instead of crying like other children, Wendy would whine. And she whined loudly—all day!

Wendy whined in the morning. *(Stretch neck of balloon to make noise and read this part with a whining voice.)* "Mommy! I can't find my teddy bear!"

"Look under your bed," Mom said. "It always falls off when you're asleep."

Wendy whined at dinner. *(Stretch neck of balloon for noise.)* "I hate vegetables! Don't make me eat vegetables! I want pizza."

"You can't have pizza every night, Wendy," Daddy said. "Now eat your vegetables."

And Wendy always whined when her friends came to play. *(Stretch neck of balloon for noise.)* "She doesn't play fair! It was my turn! She's not my friend!"

"Wendy, if you can't share, your friends won't come to play anymore," Mom said.

Wendy's parents couldn't take it anymore. When Wendy whined, they tried turning up the radio. They tried using earplugs. They even tried ignoring her.

But nothing worked. Finally, Wendy's parents sat her down for a talk.

"Wendy," Mom said. "When you're upset or angry, why don't you go to your room?"

"Yes," Dad agreed. "Instead of whining, you can punch your pillows, or stomp the floor or turn a flip."

(Stretch neck of balloon for noise.) "Ahhhhhhhhhh!"

Mom and Dad both gave Wendy a stern look. She clapped her hand over her mouth.

The next day, Wendy dropped her bubble gum in the dirt. She ran into the house. *(Stretch neck of balloon for noise.)* "Mommy! Daddy! Guess what happened!" Then, Wendy realized she was whining. She clapped her hand over her mouth and ran into her room.

Mom and Dad heard her punch the pillows and stomp the floor. Then they heard her turning flips. There were so relieved, they let out a sigh of relief. *(Let the remaining air out of the balloon quickly as you sigh.)* "Phew!"

Rabbit's Big Garden

Materials

gallon jar of water
three carrots

Presentation Idea

Cut out and color the Rabbit and Hedgehog figures. Glue to craft sticks and manipulate as the story suggests.

Explanation

The curved sides of the jar and the water together work as a convex lens that reflects (bends) light causing it to magnify.

Directions

At the designated time in the story, slowly lower carrots into the water to magnify them.

Rabbit's Big Garden

"Taking carrots from the farmer's garden is just too risky," Rabbit told his family. "I'm going to plant my own."

Rabbit found the perfect spot and set to work. He tilled the dirt, planted the seeds and watered them. Then Rabbit went home tired, but happy.

Soon, his carrots started to grow. Rabbit waited and waited and waited. And when he thought the carrots were just right, he grabbed a basket and went out to the garden to gather them.

When Rabbit got there, he couldn't believe his eyes. All of his carrots were gone! Rabbit looked over the hill just in time to see Hedgehog waddling away with them.

"Oh no!" Rabbit shouted, angrily. "I can't have Hedgehog taking my carrots! I'll just plant my garden somewhere else."

Rabbit found a spot on the other side of the hill. He tilled the ground, planted the seeds and watered them. Then he went home.

Rabbit waited and waited and waited. When he thought the carrots were just right, he took his basket and went out to the garden to gather them. But, once again, the carrots were gone. Rabbit caught a glimpse of Hedgehog dragging his carrots into the bushes.

"I don't believe it!" Rabbit shouted. "He can't get away with this! I'll move my garden again."

So Rabbit found another spot to plant his carrots. He worked just as hard as he had before, then he waited and waited and waited.

When he thought the carrots were just right, he took his basket into the garden to gather them. Again, there were no carrots. Rabbit knew who had taken them.

"That's it!" he shouted. "I have to find a way to keep Hedgehog from taking my carrots!"

Then Rabbit had a magnificent idea.

He planted his carrots at the top of the hill. He tilled the ground, planted the seeds and watered them. He was especially happy with the extra sunshine and rich soil at the hill's peak.

"This should do it," he said.

Rabbit had indeed found the perfect spot because his carrots grew bigger and bigger and bigger! (Slowly lower the carrots into the jar of water so they are magnified.) They were the biggest carrots anyone had ever seen, including Hedgehog.

"Wow!" Hedgehog shouted as he waddled up the hill. He grabbed the tops of the carrots and tried to pull them from the ground. He pulled and pulled, but the carrots were too heavy. They wouldn't budge. Hedgehog kept pulling. He refused to give up. He pulled . . . and tugged . . . and yanked. Finally, the carrots popped up from the ground and rolled down the hill, on top of Hedgehog!

"Help! Help!" Hedgehog cried. "I'm stuck!"

Rabbit heard the commotion and came running out. "Ah ha!" he said. "I knew I would catch you!"

"Help me, please" Hedgehog begged. "I can't move!"

"I'll help you on one condition."

"Anything, anything, I'll do anything!" Hedgehog pleaded.

"Promise to leave my garden alone."

"Yes, yes," Hedgehog agreed. So Rabbit called out all of his family, and they pushed the carrots back to Rabbit's house. And Rabbit never worried about his carrots again, because Hedgehog kept his promise.

Flying Fairy

Early in the morning
While the dew is on the ground,
Sneak into the meadow
And take a look around.

Hide behind the bushes;
Try not to blink too fast,
And you might see, quite fancy free,
A fairy twirling past.

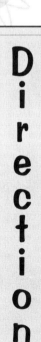

Materials

scissors
crayons or markers
paper clip

Explanation

While the fairy is dropping, the blades (wings) are getting an upward thrust of wind, pushing in opposite directions. This causes the fairy to spin.

Directions

1. Color and cut out the fairy.
2. Cut the wings down the dotted line and fold out.
3. Put a paper clip on her feet.
4. Hold the fairy high over your head and let her drop. She'll spin as she falls.

The Broken Straw

Materials

clear drinking glass about two-thirds full of water

straw

Explanation

Light rays travel more slowly through glass and water. The light from the portion of the straw in the water reaches our eyes later than the portion above the water, causing the straw to appear broken.

Directions

At designated times, place the straw into the glass of water, then remove.

The Broken Straw

Michael raced into the kitchen and poured a glass of cool water. He'd been playing baseball all afternoon, and his throat felt like a desert! He pulled out a long, skinny straw and plopped it into the glass. *(Place the straw in the water.)* As he was about to take a drink, he noticed something strange. His straw was broken!

"Oh, great," Michael said, rolling his eyes. He plucked the straw out of the water. *(Take the straw out of the water.)* To his amazement, the straw wasn't broken at all.

"That's weird," he said. *(Place the straw back in the water.)*

Michael put the straw back in. He was about to take another sip, when again, he saw the straw was broken.

"I was right," he said, raising it out of the water. *(Take the straw from the water.)*

But the dripping straw was in one piece.

"Wow! I must have been out in the sun too long," he said, blinking his eyes.

He put the straw back in the water. *(Place the straw back in the water.)* He bent down and took a close look. No doubt about it, that straw was broken. He quickly lifted it up. *(Pull the straw up fast and look it over.)*

"That's impossible," Michael said. He dropped the straw back into the water. *(Put the straw back.)* Again it was broken.

"I give up!"

Michael closed his eyes and took a long sip from the straw. *(Close your eyes and take a sip of water.)*.

"I don't believe it!" Michael shouted. "I can drink from a broken straw!"

Sunk!

Materials

clear quart jar filled three-
   fourths with water
1 fresh egg
1 cup of salt
spoon

Presentation Idea

This story lends itself to a flannel board presentation.
You will need cut-outs for fish, frog, duck, cat, dog, goat, farmer with a sack of salt and a tabletop flannel board.

Explanation

The addition of salt makes the water denser and more buoyant.

Directions

1. Hold up the egg, then drop it lightly in the jar of water.
2. Pour salt into the jar of water.
3. Stir with spoon.

Sunk!

Plop! Mrs. Hen laid an egg. *(Hold up the egg.)* The egg rolled down the hill, right into the pond. *(Lightly drop the egg into the jar of water.)*

Mrs. Hen gasped. Then she began to cry.

"Help! Help! My egg has sunk! It rolled downhill and went kerplunk!"

A fish swimming by heard the hen shout.

"I'll get your egg," he said. He swam down and grabbed the egg. He pulled and pulled, but he wasn't strong enough to pull the egg up to the top.

Again the hen cried.

"Help! Help! My egg has sunk! It rolled downhill and went kerplunk!"

A fat frog on a lily pad said, "I'll help."

He dove into the water and grabbed the fish's tail. The fish grabbed the egg, and they pulled and they pulled, but they couldn't pull the egg out of the water.

The hen cried again.

"Help! Help! My egg has sunk! It rolled downhill and went kerplunk!"

A duck said, "I'll help."

The duck grabbed the frog, the frog grabbed the fish and the fish grabbed the egg, and they pulled and they pulled, but they couldn't pull the egg out of the water.

Just then, a cat came by. She heard the hen cry.

"Help! Help! My egg has sunk! It rolled downhill and went kerplunk!"

"I'll help," the cat said.

The cat grabbed the duck, the duck grabbed the frog, the frog grabbed the fish and the fish grabbed the egg, and they pulled and they pulled, but they couldn't pull the egg out of the water.

Along came a dog. He heard the hen cry.

"Help! Help! My egg has sunk! It rolled downhill and went kerplunk!"

"I'll help," the dog said.

The dog grabbed the cat, the cat grabbed the duck, the duck grabbed the frog, the frog grabbed the fish and the fish grabbed the egg, and they pulled and they pulled, but they couldn't pull the egg out of the water.

A noisy billy goat wandered over. He heard the hen cry.

"Help! Help! My egg has sunk! It rolled downhill and went kerplunk!"

"I'll help," the billy goat said.

The goat grabbed the dog, the dog grabbed the cat, the cat grabbed the duck, the duck grabbed the frog, the frog grabbed the fish and the fish grabbed the egg, and they pulled and they pulled, then OOPS! The egg slipped out of the fish's grasp, and all the animals tumbled backwards, one on top of the other.

They stumbled right into the farmer, who happened to be walking by, carrying a large bag of salt. The bag broke and the salt poured into the pond. *(Pour the salt into the jar of water.)* The salt swirled around and around *(Stir the water with the spoon to dissolve the salt.)*, and, like magic, the egg came floating up to the top of the water.

The happy hen rolled her egg back to her nest and sat on it until it hatched.

Campfire

Materials

red food coloring
clear bowl of water

Explanation

The water separates the food coloring from the paper fibers, moving it upward to give it a fiery appearance.

It's dark here at camp,
We can't see a thing!
What's this?
Some kind of game?

We've wieners to roast,
Marshmallows to toast.
I know!
We're missing the flame!

Directions

1. Color and cut out the logs.
2. While reciting the poem, place a drop of red food coloring on top of the logs, then dip the paper into a clear bowl of water so that the campfire is completely submerged. Watch the flames rise!

The Pied Piper of Hamelin

Materials

wide drinking straw
glass of water

Explanation

Air passing across the straw vibrates. Vibrating air causes sound. Sliding the straw up and down produces different tones because the column of air inside the straw is being shortened or lengthened.

Directions

1. Place drinking straw in water.
2. At designated times, blow across the top of the straw to produce sound.
3. Slide the straw up and down for different tones.

The Pied Piper of Hamelin

Rats! Rats! Rats! They invaded the town of Hamelin. Rats in the streets! Rats in the schools! Rats in all the houses! The people of Hamelin were fed up! They stormed into the mayor's office.

"You must do something about the rats!" they protested. "If we're not rid of them soon, we'll all become sick!"

"Let me reassure you that I am doing everything I can," the mayor said, brushing a scruffy little rat off his desk. "I'm working on a plan at this very moment."

But the mayor really didn't have a plan. He felt helpless.

That night when he got into bed, he found an entire family of rats nesting on his pillow.

"Enough!" he screamed.

The next day the mayor issued a proclamation. Anyone who could rid the town of the rats would receive 1000 pieces of gold.

The people went wild. They chased the rats with brooms and sticks. They fired at them with arrows and slingshots. They even sprinkled them with pepper. Nothing worked.

Then early one morning, a man appeared in the town square. His tall, lanky body wasn't much wider than the slender flute he held in his hand.

"Where may I find the mayor?" he asked.

"Just follow this trial of rats," one man said. "The mayor has the finest garbage in Hamelin. They take turns shuffling through it every day."

The stranger followed the line of vermin right up to City Hall. He found the mayor examining a new brand of rat traps.

"Did you say you would pay 1000 gold pieces to anyone who could rid this town of rats?" the tall, wispy stranger asked.

"Indeed I did," the mayor replied.

"Good. I'll begin immediately."

The man walked to the town square, placed his flute to his lips, and began to play.

(Blow across the top of the straw, moving it up and down to create different tones.)

The rats stopped to listen. Then they jumped off the roofs. They climbed down drainpipes. They crawled across clotheslines. They hurried through the town to meet the piper. And when all the rats had gathered, the piper strolled down the road, never once stopping his gentle music. The rats followed.

The piper led them to a nearby river where each rat jumped in, one by one. And that was the end of them.

The people of Hamelin cheered and slapped the piper on the back. They waved banners and brought him sweets.

"Excellent job!" the mayor said, shaking his hand. "Here is the gold piece I promised you."

48

"But you promised me 1000 gold pieces," the piper said.

"No, no," the mayor said, laughing. "You misunderstood. The agreement was a single gold piece."

"The agreement was 1000 gold pieces," the piper argued. "And if you don't pay, you will regret it!"

The mayor turned a heated shade of red. "You would threaten the mayor? I should take you down to the river and throw you in with the rats!" he screamed. "Now leave before I arrest you for having played your flute on a public street. That's disturbing the peace!"

The piper stomped back to the town square. He lifted his flute and began to play. *(Blow across the top of the straw.)* His sweet music drifted through the air like the smell of a bakery. But now, it was the children of Hamelin that came.

They hopped out of windows. They climbed down trees. They crawled across fences. They hurried through the town to meet the piper. And when all the children had gathered, the piper walked down the road, never once stopping his music.

The children ran, skipped and danced behind him. They followed him out of Hamelin, never to be seen again.

Knowing the people would be angry, the mayor quietly packed his bags and sneaked out of town.

And now, every once in a while, when the day is calm and still, the people of Hamelin hear the whisper of a flute *(Blow on the straw.)* and the distant laughter of happy children.

The Titanic

Materials

small tub of water
large piece of ice
stiff, dry sponge

Presentation Idea

Cut your sponge into a boat shape. The sponges that are dried flat will be the easiest to cut.

Explanation

The dry sponge contains air pockets which make it lightweight and buoyant. When squeezed, the air is replaced with water, making it heavier.

Directions

1. Place ice in the tub of water.
2. Lay the dry sponge on the water and let it float.
3. Squeeze the sponge with your hand to fill it with water so it will sink.

The *Titanic*

Unsinkable! That's what the newspapers said about an amazing new ship built in 1912. The ship's name was *Titanic*, the largest ship anyone in the world had ever seen! It was as long as four city blocks, and as tall as an 11-story building. Inside were restaurants, a swimming pool, a post office and many, many fancy bedrooms. It was a floating palace!

The big day arrived. On April 10, 1912, passengers boarded the *Titanic* for its first voyage across the ocean. They were to sail from England to America. A crowd gathered on the shore to watch the *Titanic* leave. They cheered and waved flags. A band played popular music to celebrate this joyful time. The *Titanic* pulled out of the harbor and set sail.
(Lay the dry sponge on the water and let it float.)

After four days, the *Titanic* had sailed quite a long way. Then, late that night, it sailed right toward an iceberg! An alarm sounded, but it was too late for the seamen steering the ship to turn away. The *Titanic* scraped the side of the iceberg, ripping the bottom of the great ship.
(Push the sponge toward the ice and brush it along the side.)

Water poured in, flooding the decks.
(Squeeze the sponge with your hand so it will fill with water, then let it sink to the bottom of the tub.) The *Titanic* slowly sank.

To this day, the *Titanic* sits on the bottom of the ocean floor. The great ship everyone thought was unsinkable will never float again.

Amanda's Imaginary Friend

Materials

piece of black construction
     paper
slightly moistened cotton swab

Directions

1. Draw a smiling face on the construction paper.
2. At the end of the story, hold up the paper to show the face has disappeared.

Explanation

The molecules in water move about continuously. They escape into the air, changing from liquid to gas, becoming water vapor. This process is evaporation.

Amanda's Imaginary Friend

Cookie was more than Amanda's best friend. *(Draw a smiley face on the construction paper with the wet cotton swab.)* She was Amanda's imaginary friend. Only Amanda could see her. And everywhere Amanda went, Cookie tagged along. *(Lay the construction paper down until the end of the story.)*

When they went to the park, Amanda pushed Cookie on the swing. At the grocery store, Amanda would get a chocolate chip cookie for herself and a peanut butter cookie for Cookie. And at night, Amanda and Cookie would lie in bed and look at picture books together.

When water splashed out of the bathtub, Amanda said, "Cookie did it!"

When the lamp fell off the corner table and broke, Amanda said, "Cookie did it!"

And when Amanda spilled mud pies on her pink overalls, she burst into the house shouting, "Cookie did it! Cookie did it!"

It seemed Amanda couldn't eat, sleep or breathe without Cookie.

"Amanda, aren't you getting too old to have an imaginary playmate?" her mother asked.

"Cookie is my best friend!" Amanda cried.

Then, the first day of school arrived. Amanda spent the day finger painting, learning new songs and writing her ABCs. When her mother picked her up that afternoon, Amanda shouted, "School was fun! We did so much, and I met a lot of kids."

"Did Cookie like it?" Mother asked with a smile.

Amanda felt a little guilty. She had been so busy, she hadn't thought of Cookie all day.

"She liked it okay," she said quietly.

Day after day passed. Amanda mentioned Cookie less and less. Then during the Thanksgiving holidays, Amanda went to the grocery store with her mother. She ran to the bakery section to get a chocolate chip cookie.

"Aren't you going to get one for Cookie?" her mother asked.

"Mom!" Amanda said, "I'm a big girl now."

"What happened to Cookie?" her mother asked.

"Cookie's gone."

(Hold up the construction paper to show that the picture has disappeared.)

Itsy Bitsy Spider

The itsy bitsy spider climbed up the water spout.
Down came the rain and washed the spider out.
Out came the sun and dried up all the rain.
And the itsy bitsy spider climbed up the spout again.

Materials

scissors
crayons or
    markers
12" of string
hole punch
straw
flashlight
clear glass of
    water

Explanation

The top of the straw is sealed off, which lessens the air pressure above the straw. The greater pressure of air under the straw holds the water in.

Directions

1. Color and cut out the spider.
2. Punch a hole in the top and tie on the string.
3. Have a student volunteer help by holding the flashlight toward the glass.
4. Place the straw in the glass of water with your finger covering the top to keep air from getting into the straw.
5. As you sing the song, slowly raise the straw up from the water, and raise the spider on the string next to it to look like he's climbing the straw.
6. While singing "Down came the rain," lift your finger to let the water pour out of the straw and back into the glass.
7. While singing "Out came the sun," have the child turn on the flashlight to represent the sun.

The Dry Snail

Materials

clear bowl of water
glass or jar

A squiggly, squirmy snail
Curled up inside her shell,
Then sank deep down
Below the ocean tide.

Beneath the sea and foam
She stayed inside her home.
And not a drop
Of water leaked inside!

Explanation

Water cannot get in because the
glass is already full of air.

Directions

1. Copy page 57.
2. While reciting the poem, crumble the picture of
   the snail and stuff it into the glass, snugly
   enough so it doesn't fall out when turned
   upside down.
3. Holding the glass bottom up, plunge it straight
   down into the bowl and hold it there.
4. Once you've finished the poem, lift the glass
   out and remove the paper. The snail will still be
   dry.

The Ambitious Raisins

Materials

6 raisins
tall, clear glass or jar
1 cup of water
$\frac{1}{2}$ cup of vinegar
1 tablespoon of baking soda

Explanation

Baking soda reacting with vinegar produces carbon dioxide gas. The gas bubbles collect around the raisin's skin. When completely coated with the bubbles, the raisins rise to the surface. There, the bubbles exposed to air burst. When there are not enough bubbles to support them, the raisins sink.

Directions

1. Place six raisins in the bottom of the jar.
2. Pour in one cup of water and one-half cup of vinegar.
3. At the designated moment, pour in the baking soda.

The Ambitious Raisins

Six raisins sat lazily in the bottom of a jar.

"You know what I'm going to be when I grow up?" one raisin bragged. "A tasty snack. Then I can travel to school in a lunch box, and see the inside of a cafeteria. What an adventure!"

"That sounds exciting," said another, "but I have a better plan. I'm going to sneak into an oatmeal cookie. Then I can go on a picnic and see the outside world. Experience nature. Breathe fresh air."

"Wouldn't that be great?" said a third raisin. "But I think I would rather be in an ice cream sundae. What could be better than sitting on top of a cool ice cream mountain, floating down a river of oozing chocolate? And think of the fun I'll have hanging out with a bunch of nuts."

"No ice cream for me," the fourth raisin complained. "I can't stand the cold. I'd rather be wrapped in a soft, warm cinnamon roll. Nothing could be more cozy and relaxing. I'd curl up and sleep all day."

"How boring!" Raisin Five shouted. "If I have a choice, you can bet I'm going to end up in a breakfast cereal. Swimming around in a large bowl of milk is more my style. Well yeah, you have to hang out with some real flakes, but nothing's perfect, right?"

"Forget it, guys" the last raisin said. "You're daydreaming for nothing. We've already been chosen for something special."

"What?" the others asked, anxiously.

"We were picked to be the characters in this story." *(Pour in the tablespoon of baking soda.)*

The raisins bubbled with excitement. *(The baking soda and vinegar will fizz.)*

Then they jumped for joy! *(The raisins will float up and down in the jar.)*

The Magic Pot

Materials

clear jar filled one-fourth full with baking soda
vinegar
teaspoon
tray

Presentation Idea

Several versions of this story are available in picture book form. *Big Anthony and the Magic Pasta Pot* by Tomie de Paola is one your students might enjoy.

Explanation

Baking soda and vinegar together produce carbon dioxide gas which foams and bubbles.

Directions

1. Place the jar on the tray for easy cleanup.
2. Place one teaspoon of vinegar into the baking soda.
3. Slowly pour in a generous amount of vinegar until the jar overflows.

60

The Magic Pot

A German Folktale

Many years ago a young girl named Inga lived with her mother in a small village near the forest. Because they were poor, Inga would go into the woods every day to search for nuts and berries to eat.

One day, as Inga dug through the bushes, she saw an old woman hobbling by. The woman was heaving an iron pot. Inga rushed over.

"May I help you carry that?" she asked. "It looks too heavy for you."

The woman was touched by Inga's kindness. "Sweet child, you shall not be hungry again," she said, with a smile. "I want you to take this pot, and whenever you want something to eat, just say, 'Boil, boil, little pot!' and the pot will fill with steaming, delicious porridge. When you've had enough say, 'Stop, stop, little pot!' and the pot will stop cooking."

"Thank you! Thank you!" Inga cried, giving the old woman a hug.

When Inga got home, her mother was gone. She set the pot on the table and said, "Boil, boil, little pot!" And right before her eyes the little pot began to boil. *(Drop a teaspoon of vinegar into the jar of baking soda so that it will boil slightly.)* Inga ate and ate until she couldn't eat another bite. Then she said, "Stop, stop, little pot!" And immediately the pot stopped boiling.

When her mother came home, Inga made some more porridge in the magic pot.

"Boil, boil, little pot!"

(Pour another teaspoon of vinegar into the baking soda so that it will boil slightly.)

Again they ate until they were stuffed. Then Inga took the pot away and said the magic words, "Stop, stop, little pot!" The pot stopped.

Everything was fine for a time, but one day while Inga was out gathering fire- wood, her mother decided to make por- ridge. "Boil, boil, little pot!" she com- manded. And the pot went right to work. But the mother didn't know the words to stop the pot. *(Slowly pour in a generous amount of vinegar until it overflows the jar. Continue pouring until the solution overflows sever- al times.)* The porridge poured over the edge onto the table.

"Enough," Mother said.

But the pot kept boiling.

Then it spilled onto the floor!

"Quit!" Mother shouted.

But the pot continued to boil.

Inga's mother tried and tried to stop the pot, but it was no use. She didn't know the magic words. The porridge flowed out of the kitchen and into the streets. Soon the whole village was flooded with por- ridge.

"Oh no!" Inga said, seeing the river of por- ridge.

She waded back to her house, her feet heavy in the mush.

"Stop, stop, little pot!" she said.

Instantly, the pot stopped. The people in the village cleaned up the porridge, then one by one, they came and thanked Inga and her mother. They all agreed, it was the most they'd eaten in a long time!

Bluebird
Traditional Nursery Rhyme

Bluebird, bluebird, through my window.
Bluebird, bluebird, through my window.
Bluebird, bluebird, through my window.
Oh, Johnny, I'm so tired.

Materials

scissors
glue
crayons or markers
string or thread
hole punch

Directions

1. Copy the picture below and cut out.
2. Color the bird and window curtains with crayons.
3. Fold in half so that circles and tabs match up.
4. Glue together.
5. Punch a hole on each tab and thread the string through.
6. Twirl it to make the bird appear at the window.

Explanation

The eye continues to see each object a moment after it disappears. The eye and the brain mix the two, causing them to appear as one.

Observation Page

1. Name which parts of the story were demonstrated. _____

2. Can you describe the materials used? _____

3. Where might you find the things used to show the story?_____

   _____

4. Was the story demonstration colorful? _____

5. Did it have a smell? _____

6. What do you think caused the reaction?_____

   _____

7. Did you learn a new science word from this story?_____

8. Draw a picture of the story.